Contents

KT-499-472

This manual is designed to be used on The Marriage Course with the DVDs or live talks. See page 131 for more information on how to join or run a course.

The Marriage Course

Guest Manual

© Alpha International 2015

First edition published 2001

This revised edition 2015
10 9 8 7 6 5 4 3 2 1

ISBN 978-1-909309-37-1

Published by Alpha International, HTB Brompton Road, London SW7 1JA.

publications@alpha.org

Acknowledgements

We are very grateful indeed to the following people and organisations
for their help and inspiration in the creation of The Marriage Course:

David and Teresa Ferguson, of Intimate Life Ministries, whose expertise and
encouragement have helped us enormously, especially with Sessions 1 and 4.
For more information about their work, contact: Intimate Life Ministries, 2511
S. Lakeline Blvd, Austin, Texas, TX78759; or visit greatcommandment.net

Rob Parsons, for his inspiration, stories and illustrations that we have used
throughout. For more information about his work, please visit
careforthefamily.org.uk

Gary Chapman, for his book *The Five Love Languages* (Northfield, 1992),
on which the concept and manual notes for Session 7 are based.

Peter and Barbie Reynolds, for their demonstration of effective listening,
the inspiration for the model example in Session 2.

Acorn Christian Foundation, for their *Just Listen!* course, on which much
of the material on listening in Session 2 is based. For more information about
their work, please visit acornchristian.org

Michael and Gillie Warren, for the first marriage weekend that they led, where
we learnt many of the basic principles for building a healthy marriage.

Nicky and Sila Lee

Building Strong Foundations

EXERCISE 1

The First Time You Met

Tell each other your strongest memory of the first time you met and what first attracted you to one another.

What is marriage?

- Marriage involves a man and a woman being joined together and becoming one
- A relationship of increasing intimacy and growing interdependence

'For this reason a man will leave his father and mother and be united to his wife, and they will become one flesh.'

Genesis 2:24

The four seasons of marriage

(Not every marriage will go through each stage, but the principles apply to all marriages)

1. Spring
- Early years of marriage
- Season of discovery and excitement
- Initial infatuation will wear off at some stage
- The greatest need is to accept each other

2. Summer

- Season of increased activity and demands
- May become parents during this season
- May face pressures of infertility
- Careers can be more demanding
- The greatest need is to give time to the marriage relationship

---

Marriage:
The closest possible human relationship of growing interdependence.

---

3. Autumn

- Season of richness and maturity – reaping the benefits of what has gone before
- Marriage more established having weathered tough times
- May be teenagers in the house – emotionally the most exhausting stage of parenting
- The greatest need is to support and encourage each other

Notes

4. Winter

- Empty-nest stage for many
- Probably fewer demands with an opportunity for more time together
- Can be the most exciting stage of marriage
- The greatest needs are shared interests and good communication

Why do some marriages break down?

- A process of growing apart
- A lack of communication
- Consumerism – the failure to work at a relationship

Working Through Pressures

Reflect on what you've heard so far. Talk together about the pressures you've worked through until now in your relationship, and the pressures you're currently facing.

The aim of The Marriage Course

To help couples grow closer through:

- Choosing commitment to each other and to their marriage
- Spending time looking at relevant issues together
- Increasing their understanding of each other
- Developing good habits

The marriage wheel

'Love and faithfulness
meet together...'

Psalm 85:10

Taking Stock of Your Marriage

Read through the list of statements and, using the scale below, write in the box the number that you feel corresponds to your viewpoint. Please do the exercise on your own. When you have finished, turn over and follow the instructions overleaf.

0. never true	**1.** rarely true	**2.** occasionally true	**3.** usually true	**4.** always true

I feel that...

1. My partner regularly gives me their undivided attention ☐

2. My partner understands and supports my beliefs and values ☐

3. My partner shows me affection through demonstrative non-sexual touching ☐

4. We are able to apologise and forgive when one of us has hurt the other ☐

5. My partner listens to my point of view even when we disagree ☐

6. I am able to talk to my partner about my sexual hopes and desires ☐

7. I am able to talk to my partner about my hopes and dreams for the future ☐

8. My partner is good at encouraging me in what I do ☐

9. We make it a priority to go out together at least once a fortnight ☐

10. We often reflect on the good things we enjoy as a couple ☐

11. We are able to talk about strong emotions such as excitement, hope, grief and anxiety ☐

12. My partner is sensitive towards my sexual needs ☐

13. My partner encourages me in my spiritual growth ☐

14. My partner is good at meeting my emotional needs ☐

15. We agree on our sexual practices ☐

16. We discuss new ideas with each other ☐

17. We support each other in the goals we have for our family life ☐

18. We have a number of joint interests that we pursue together ☐

19. I am happy about the frequency of our lovemaking ☐

20. My partner is good at listening to my feelings without interrupting or criticising me ☐

Please turn over ⟶

Results of Taking Stock of Your Marriage

1. Add up your scores from the previous page as follows:

Add up your scores for statements	My score	Partner's score
4, 8, 9, 14 and 18	☐	☐
1, 5, 11, 16 and 20	☐	☐
3, 6, 12, 15 and 19	☐	☐
2, 7, 10, 13 and 17	☐	☐

2. Now look at each other's scores and discuss them, especially any differences (the idea is to be understood by and to understand each other better).

3. Take it in turns to tell each other something in each area that you would like to see changed in yourself.

For example:

Friendship:
'I see that I haven't recognised the need for us to spend time together on our own. What could I do to change that?'

Communication:
'I don't seem to be very good at listening.
I obviously need to show you that I am interested in what you say.'

Physical relationship:
'I would like to be more sensitive towards your sexual desires.
What could I do?'

The future:
'We haven't had a conversation for a long time about our plans for the future. When would be a good time for that?'

Building the foundations for a strong marriage

1. Make time for each other

If a relationship is to thrive and keep growing, we must have regular time together.

At the very least, plan to spend 1–2 hours alone together each week to rekindle romance, to have fun, to talk together about your feelings (eg, your hopes, fears, worries, excitements). We call this *marriage time*.

Marriage time should have all the connotations of a 'date' together.

The benefits of marriage time

- Keeps the fun and romance alive in our relationship
- Deepens our understanding and appreciation of each other
- Ensures we communicate regularly on a meaningful level

Golden rule:
Never change your marriage time without consulting your partner.

Notes

How to make marriage time happen

1. Plan time together

   It doesn't happen automatically. Find the best time for you and book it in, just like you would any other social or business appointment.

   Write it in your calendars eg: Monday evening, 'marriage time' or Wednesday lunchtime, 'marriage time'. If you are very busy, plan marriage time several months in advance.

2. Prioritise your time together

   Make marriage time a commitment that you stick to every week. It should take priority over other demands such as work, going out with friends, playing sport and even parenting.

3. Protect your time together

   Protect this time from interruptions and distractions such as the telephone, the computer, visitors, the television and over-long working hours.

'Prioritising marriage time is constantly the most difficult thing that we struggle to do, but the most important in terms of how it impacts our relationship.'

**Couple on
The Marriage Course**

EXERCISE 4

Special Times Together

Tell your partner what have been the most special times you have shared together as a couple. Be specific. Explain why they were special to you.

'The Lord God said, "It is not good for the man to be alone. I will make a helper suitable for him."'

Genesis 2:18

2. Nurture each other

- Nurturing involves seeking to meet each other's emotional needs for affection, encouragement, support, comfort, etc
- We all have a longing to be loved and to be known by another
- Empty space inside that needs to be filled up with love
- When empty, we feel alone or lonely
- Giving each other emotional support refills the empty space inside
- We are made for close relationships

How to nurture

Be proactive rather than reactive:
- Being reactive means focusing on each other's shortcomings
- Being proactive means focusing on each other's needs
- Proactive behaviour draws couples together because each one feels loved. When we feel loved, we feel like loving

Study each other:
- Recognise each other's needs
- Often our partner's needs and desires will be different to our own
- Discover what matters to your husband or wife. Otherwise we tend to give what we like to receive
- Needs change over time
- Make requests, not demand
- We can't assume our husband or wife automatically knows our desires. We must tell each other

'Husbands... live with your wives in an understanding way.'

1 Peter 3:7 (NASB)

EXERCISE 5

Knowing Me, Knowing You

Please read through the list on the next page.

1. In column A, tick the three that matter most to you (ie, what you would most like your husband or wife to give to you).

2. In column B, tick the three that you believe matter most to your husband or wife (ie, what you think they would most like to receive from you).

   NB: There is some overlap between the different desires – put those three which most clearly express your preferences.

3. When you have both finished, exchange your responses and see how well you understand your husband or wife.

   - How close were you to selecting the three that matter most to your husband or wife?

   - How many of the same desires did you and your partner put for yourselves? 0, 1, 2 or 3?

   - Consider which, if any, of the list of desires you tend to give least to your husband or wife. Are these any of the three that matter most to your partner?

EXERCISE 5 (continued)

	A Myself (choose 3)	B My partner (choose 3)
Affirmation – being appreciated for who you are by your partner	☐	☐
Approval – being commended for those things you have done well	☐	☐
Companionship – doing things together and sharing experiences	☐	☐
Conversation – talking together about issues of interest and importance	☐	☐
Encouragement – being inspired to keep going through your partner's words	☐	☐
Openness – being confident of your partner's honesty about every aspect of their lives, including their feelings and ideas	☐	☐
Physical affection – the communication of care and closeness through physical touch	☐	☐
Practical help – experiencing your partner's help in big or small tasks	☐	☐
Presents – receiving tangible expressions of love and thoughtfulness	☐	☐
Respect – having your ideas and opinions considered and valued by your partner	☐	☐
Security – facing the future confident of your partner's commitment to love you and stay with you	☐	☐
Sexual intimacy – having regular opportunities to express and receive love through your sexual relationship	☐	☐
Support – knowing your partner is working with you to fulfil your goals	☐	☐
Time together – knowing your partner has set aside time to be with you on a regular basis	☐	☐
Understanding – knowing your partner is aware of what matters to you	☐	☐
Undivided attention – focusing on each other to the exclusion of any distractions	☐	☐

Marriage Time
Session 1 – Homework

Set aside two hours of marriage time together sometime before the next session for the following two exercises.

EXERCISE 1
Planning to Succeed

Each of you write down your answers to the following questions. When you have both finished, show each other what you have written and then discuss your answers.

A. Time together

1. How much time do you set aside to spend alone together to build your marriage:

- on a daily basis?

- on a weekly basis?

- on an annual basis?

EXERCISE 1 (continued)

2. How much time could you be spending together regularly, and
    when:

• on a daily basis?
  *eg: 20 minutes to talk together when we get home in the evening or 10 minutes
  in the morning to plan the day*

_____

• on a weekly basis?
  *eg: every Friday night to go out together or Monday evening to spend time at
  home talking over a meal*

_____

• on an annual basis?
  *eg: go away for a long weekend as a couple or have an annual mini-
  honeymoon*

_____

B. Shared interests
1. What interests do you have in common?
   (Think back to what you did when you first went out together)
   *eg: visiting art galleries, playing a sport, exploring new places, going to the
   cinema*

_____

_____

_____

Please turn over →

EXERCISE 1 (continued)

2. Which of these interests do you pursue together as a couple now?
   How regularly?
   How much time do you set aside for them?
   eg: playing tennis – once a fortnight – two hours

_____

_____

_____

3. Are there other mutual interests you would benefit from pursuing together now?

_____

_____

_____

C. Separate interests

1. What interests do you encourage your partner to pursue that you do not share?

_____

_____

2. What interests do you pursue that your partner does not share?

_____

_____

EXERCISE 1 (continued)

3. Are there other separate interests that you or your partner would like to pursue?

You: _____

_____

Your partner: _____

_____

D. Annual holidays

1. Which have been your best holidays together and why?

_____

_____

_____

2. Suggest an idea for a holiday/time away together in the future

_____

_____

_____

Please turn over→

EXERCISE 2

Showing Love

1. Write down what you remember to be your husband's or wife's top three desires from the exercise 'Knowing Me, Knowing You' on page 14.

1. _____

2. _____

3. _____

Now write down your own three main desires and give examples of how your husband or wife could meet them for you.

For example:

My desires	How my partner could meet them
Conversation	Initiate conversation when we are having a meal together by asking me questions about my day
Approval	Tell me when I have done something well at home or at work. Show that you notice when I have made an effort
Time together	Take the initiative in suggesting we go out together. Sit down with me for 30 minutes each evening to talk about the day
Physical affection	Hug and kiss me when we see each other after time apart. Hold me in bed before we go to sleep
Presents	Give me a present when I least expect it

EXERCISE 2 (continued)

My desires   **How my partner could meet them**

1. _____   _____

    _____

    _____

2. _____   _____

    _____

    _____

3. _____   _____

    _____

    _____

- Show each other what you have written
- In the coming weeks, try to concentrate on meeting your husband's or wife's desires rather than criticising him or her for not meeting yours

The Art of Communication

The Art of Communication

Introduction
- Intimacy requires effective communication
- We all have a longing to be known
- The Marriage Course is designed to help couples communicate both during and between the sessions

Effective communication
- Communication involves the message, the speaker and the listener
- Building intimacy in marriage involves hearing each other's experiences, thoughts, feelings and desires

The importance of talking

- Telling each other our thoughts and feelings
- May have been taught to hide feelings during upbringing
- Will take courage and practise to re-learn how to talk about feelings
- Some have difficulty recognising what they are feeling
  (if this describes you, please see the optional homework exercise: 'Identifying Emotions', page 32)

EXERCISE 1

Barriers to Talking

Take a few minutes to look together at the diagram below and tell each other if any of the barriers apply to you.

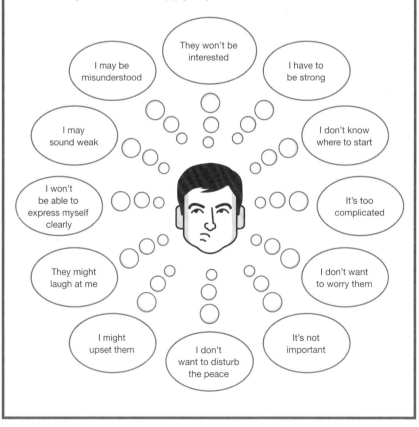

The importance of listening

- We can become highly selective in our listening
- Most of us take listening for granted, yet it is possible to close our ears
- Listening has the power to make our husband or wife feel loved and valued
- One of the most important skills to learn for a strong marriage
- The Bible places great value on listening effectively

'My dear brothers and sisters, take note of this: Everyone should be quick to listen, slow to speak and slow to become angry.'

James 1:19

EXERCISE 2

The Power of Listening

Discuss the following questions as a couple:

- How do you feel when you are listened to?
- How do you feel when you are not listened to?
- To whom would you go if you needed a listening ear?
- What makes that person a good listener?

'If I were to summarise in one sentence the single most important principle I have learned in the field of interpersonal relations, it would be this: seek first to understand, then to be understood.'

Stephen Covey

'Those who answer before listening – that is their folly and their shame.'

Proverbs 18:13

Hindrances to listening

1. Filters

- We all listen through filters but often we are unaware of them
- When someone is speaking, our own memories, attitudes, prejudices, physical environment, lack of interest, etc all affect what we hear
- Some of the time we are listening more to ourselves than to the other person
- Effective communication requires us to control the conversation in our mind

2. Bad habits

- Reassuring
- Giving advice
- Intellectualising
- Going off on a tangent
- Interrupting

- These habits can prevent the speaker from saying what they're feeling and they may eventually shut down
- We need to listen first, before coming in with our contribution

Notes

EXERCISE 3

Identifying Bad Habits

Take a few moments to identify your particular bad habit and then discuss this with your husband or wife.

EXERCISE 4

A Significant Memory

- Take it in turns to spend one minute telling your husband or wife about a happy memory of something that happened to you before you met

- The listener should then summarise what they have heard, taking particular care to describe their partner's feelings. This will show that they have been listening and empathising with what their partner felt

Notes

Principles for effective listening

For some people, learning to listen is as difficult as learning a foreign language, but we must learn in order to build intimacy in our marriage and grow closer to our husband or wife.

1. Pay attention and do not interrupt

Allow your partner to finish what they are saying. Research indicates that the average individual only listens for 17 seconds before interrupting. Maintain eye contact and do not do something else at the same time.

2. Try to put yourself in your partner's shoes

Put your own views to one side and really appreciate what it is like for your partner to be feeling the way that they do. Do not rush them and do not be afraid of silences.

3. Acknowledge their feelings

When you have listened to what your partner wants to say, reflect back what you heard without deflection or interpretation. It is important to try and accurately summarise the main facts, reflecting back any feelings they've expressed. This helps your partner to know if you have understood. 'Reflecting back' may feel awkward, but it works!

'The first service that one owes to others in fellowship consists of listening to them. Just as love of God begins with listening to his word, so the beginning of love for the brethren is learning to listen to them.'

Dietrich Bonhoeffer

Notes

4. Find out what is most important

Then ask your husband or wife: 'What is the most important part of what you have been saying?' Wait quietly while your partner thinks about what they want to say. When they have spoken, reflect back again what you have heard.

5. Help them work out what they might do

Now ask: 'Is there anything you would like (or, if appropriate: like me / like us) to do about what you have said?' Again give your partner time to think quietly. When they have finished, reflect back what your partner has said, enabling them to hear their own decision. The listener then asks, 'Is there anything more that you would like to say?' If there is anything more, this should also be reflected back to the speaker.

There is no one who is more important to listen to than our husband or wife.

EXERCISE 5

Effective Listening

Each of you pick an issue currently upsetting or bothering you that you have not discussed recently. At this point, choose an issue where there has not already been disagreement and conflict. It could be an area of concern related to work, holidays, children, your home, etc.

- The speaker should hold a table napkin (or something similar). This is to remind you whose issue is being discussed
- The speaker tells the listener about the issue and how they feel about it (do not go on for too long). The listener listens and then reflects back
- Then the listener asks, *'What is the most important aspect of what you are saying?'* The speaker responds. The listener listens and then reflects back again
- The listener then asks, *'Is there anything you would like* (or, if appropriate: *like me / like us*) *to do about what you have just said?'* Again the listener listens and then reflects back
- Finally, the listener asks, *'Is there anything more that you would like to say?'* The listener listens and then reflects back again

Then switch roles so you both have a chance to speak and to listen. This exercise is good practice for all of us both in talking about our emotions and in listening to each other.

Marriage Time
Session 2 – Homework

Each of you should complete the exercise below, 'How Good is Your Communication?' Compare what you have written.

Next, pick an area of your marriage that you haven't discussed in any depth. Then follow the steps for Exercise 5, 'Effective Listening' (page 29). Please ensure that both of you are ready to do this and are willing to follow the steps. Take it in turns to be the speaker and the listener.

Follow the guidelines as listener and speaker as you work through each other's issue. Some of you may experience a strong emotional reaction to what your partner is saying. Try to put your own reaction to one side and keep listening and reflecting back what your partner is feeling.

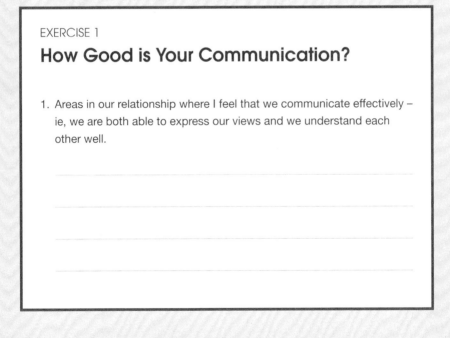

EXERCISE 1

How Good is Your Communication?

1. Areas in our relationship where I feel that we communicate effectively – ie, we are both able to express our views and we understand each other well.

EXERCISE 1 (continued)

2. Areas where we do communicate, but not well enough – ie, I feel that there is room for improvement.

_____

_____

_____

3. Areas where we are not communicating at all – whether due to neglect, embarrassment or fear.

_____

_____

_____

Suggested topics for consideration:

- Handling children
- Money matters
- Goals and directions in life
- Sex – frequency or quality
- Family planning / how many children
- Jobs around the home
- Relatives and in-laws
- Death and bereavement
- Job or career / time at work
- Church involvement
- Expressing affection and emotions
- Relaxation and rest

Please turn over →

Identifying Emotions

- To help those who struggle to identify what they are feeling
- Completing the partial sentences on the following pages will help you identify your emotions and become more emotionally aware

1. Quickly add a few words to describe your feelings (either positive or negative) for each sentence. The lists below will help you to get started.

Positive emotions

accepted	encouraged	loved	supported
appreciated	excited	liberated	sure
calm	forgiven	peaceful	trusting
capable	free	positive	understood
carefree	grateful	relaxed	valuable
comforted	happy	relieved	worthwhile
confident	hopeful	respected	
content	humbled	safe	
delighted	joyful	secure	

Negative emotions

abandoned	disappointed	jealous	unappreciated
afraid	disgusted	lonely	unloved
angry	disrespected	misunderstood	upset
anxious	dissatisfied	nervous	used
annoyed	embarrassed	numb	useless
apologetic	exposed	overwhelmed	vulnerable
ashamed	frustrated	pressured	weak
bored	guilty	rejected	
confused	humiliated	resentful	
cross	hurt	sad	
defeated	insecure	scared	
depressed	insignificant	sorrowful	

EXERCISE 2 (continued)

When we set off on holiday, I feel...

_____

When we go out with friends, I feel...

_____

When I'm in a room with people I don't know, I feel...

_____

When I'm with my parents, I feel...

_____

When I think of past successes, I feel...

_____

When I think of mistakes I've made, I feel...

_____

When I think of the future, I feel...

_____

When I think of relating to God, I feel...

_____

When my husband / wife tells me he / she loves me, I feel...

_____

When my husband / wife and I have a disagreement, I feel...

_____

Please turn over

EXERCISE 2 (continued)

When my husband / wife tells me something I've done that's disappointed or hurt him / her, I feel...

_____

When my husband / wife apologises to me, I feel...

2. Complete the following sentences

I feel most loved when...

_____

I get angry when...

_____

I feel happiest when...

_____

I am sad when...

_____

Now show your husband or wife what you have put.

3. Tell your husband or wife about a time when you felt:

- Encouraged
- Discouraged
- Understood
- Misunderstood
- Accepted
- Rejected

3 Resolving Conflict

Building Strong Foundations

- Make marriage time a weekly priority in your diaries
- Discover and seek to meet your partner's needs (see 'Knowing Me, Knowing You', page 14)

The Art of Communication

- Talk about your feelings with your partner this week
- Listen to your partner's feelings without interrupting, criticising or offering advice

Resolving Conflict

Introduction

Why is some conflict inevitable in every marriage?

- We are different – different backgrounds, priorities, desires, personalities, opinions
- No good trying to force our partner to do things our way
- Must see ourselves as being on the same side (as in a 3-legged race)
- We are naturally self-centered
- Need to ask ourselves, 'Are there ways I need to change for the sake of our partnership?'

Principles for handling conflict

1. Express appreciation of each other

- Make your husband or wife feel like the most important person in the world to you
- Focus on what you like and admire about your partner
- Express gratitude for what your partner does
- Show appreciation for who your partner is
- Make it a daily discipline

Showing Appreciation

Write down six things you appreciate about your husband or wife. (Be specific: it may be thanking them for what they do, or it may be expressing your appreciation for who they are – try to make it a mixture – looking particularly for things you may have come to take for granted.)

For example:

- How do you feel when you are listened to?
- How do you feel when you are not listened to?
- To whom would you go if you needed a listening ear?
- What makes that person a good listener?

'I love the way you get on so well with other people.'
'I love the way you're so affectionate towards me.'
'Thank you for working so hard to provide for our family.'
'Thank you for making our home such a welcoming place to be.'
'I really appreciate it that you fill the car up with petrol.'

When you have both finished, show each other what you have put.

1. _____

2. _____

3. _____

4. _____

5. _____

6. _____

'Accept one another then,
just as Christ accepted you...'

Romans 15:7

2. Identify and accept differences

- Recognise differences of temperament, personality, upbringing and values
- Don't try to change each other
- See your marriage as a partnership in which you combine your strengths and support each other's weaknesses
- Maintain a sense of humour

EXERCISE 2

Recognising Your Differences

1. Mark against each issue where on the line your partner's and your own preferences each lie, eg *(N = Nicky; S = Sila).*

	S	N
Money	Spend	Save

ISSUE	**PREFERENCE**	
Clothes	Casual	Formal
Disagreements	Thrash it out	Keep the peace
Holidays	Seek adventure	Seek rest
Money	Spend	Save
People	Time with others	Time alone
Planning	Make plans and stick to them	Be spontaneous / go with the flow
Punctuality	Have time in hand	Cut it fine
Relaxation	Go out	Be at home
Sleeping	Go to bed late	Get up early
Sports	Enthusiast	Uninterested
Telephone	Talk at length	Only for making arrangements
Tidiness	Keep everything tidy / under control	Be relaxed and live in a mess
TV	Keep it on	Throw it out

Other differences: _____

2. Show each other what you have put. Then find one issue where your differences can be a source of strength for your relationship.

3. Learn to negotiate

For some people, learning to listen is as difficult as learning a foreign language, but we must learn in order to build intimacy in our marriage and grow closer to our husband or wife.

Notes

Six Practical Steps to Peace

1. Find the best time (the 10 o'clock rule)

2. Identify the issue

3. Discuss the issue rather than attack each other

   - avoid labelling
     (eg, 'you never...' 'you always...')

   - use 'I' statements
     (eg, 'I feel undervalued when...')

   - listen to your partner
     (allow them to hold the table napkin when speaking as described in Session 2)

4. Work out possible solutions (make a list if necessary)

5. Decide on the best solution for now and see if it works

6. Be prepared to re-evaluate if there still seems to be conflict over the issue

4. Grow together

- We're not incompatible unless we refuse to change
- We can change ourselves; we cannot change each other
- We can only change when we know what matters to each other
- We must tell each other what frustrates and hurts us
- Much conflict arises from our different assumptions about the way things should be done
- Important to be aware of our own and each other's values (often learnt during our upbringing)
- Requesting change is helpful; demanding change is harmful

'Why do you look at the speck of sawdust in the other person's eye and pay no attention to the plank in your own eye?'

Matthew 7:3

EXERCISE 3

Matching Our Strides

Please turn to page 44 and complete Exercise 3 – 'Matching Our Strides – Part One'

Unrealistic expectations

When we expect our partner to meet all our needs, we inevitably fail each other and get hurt, causing our marriage to spiral downwards (see Diagram 1 below).

Diagram 1

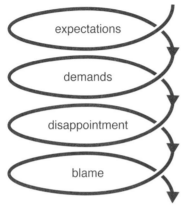

expectations

demands

disappointment

blame

When we look to God to meet our needs for significance, security and self-esteem, we are better able to give to each other (see Diagram 2 below).

Diagram 2

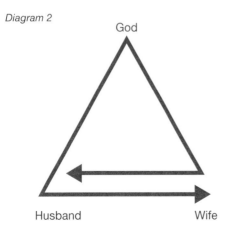

God

Husband

Wife

'God is our refuge and strength, an ever-present help in trouble.'

Psalm 46:1

5. Praying together

- Helps us connect with each other in a meaningful way
- Ensure prayers are vertical, not horizontal and manipulative
- Five to ten minutes a day is generally better than one hour every month
- Ask each other, 'What can I pray for you today?'
- Accept the same requests day after day
- Draw on God's promises from the Bible and start with thankfulness
- Don't give up even if you have young children
- The closer each of us is individually in our relationship with God, the closer we are to each other as husband and wife
- If one has upset the other, say sorry before praying
- Be deliberate and plan it into your schedule
- If you're not comfortable praying, find other ways to connect and support each other on a daily basis

'A cord of three strands is not quickly broken.'

Ecclesiastes 4:12

This describes a husband and wife with God at the centre of their relationship. (To explore this further, consider doing Alpha together – please refer to the last page for more information.)

Notes

Supporting each other
Ask your husband or wife if there's one thing they're concerned about at the moment. Then, if you're comfortable praying, pray for each other – aloud or silently. Otherwise, express your support in some other way.

Matching Our Strides – Part One

Money and Possessions

1. Each of you circle the phrases that best describe your feelings (and the messages you received from your family) about money and possessions as you grew up.

• Scrimped and saved • Had everything we wanted • Had everything we needed	• Broken things mended • Broken things thrown away	• Always short of money • Always enough money
• Worried about family running out of money • No worries about money	• Encouraged to give money / possessions away • Saved as much as possible	• Enjoyed shopping – seen as a leisure activity • Shopping kept to a minimum
• Money spent only on essentials • Money spent on luxuries	• Credit cards made use of • Credit cards avoided	• Loved getting presents • Loved giving presents
• Took plenty of time to relax • Adults always working	• Taught how to save money • Not taught how to save money	• Confident handling money • Confusion or fear about money
• Felt self-sufficient as a family • Money / bills caused arguments	• Family finances remained a mystery • Family finances explained	• As a child given allowance / taught to handle money • Adults handled all money

EXERCISE 3 (continued)

Other significant words / phrases that describe your attitude to money and possessions now:

_____

_____

_____

Show each other what you have put and discuss any differences.

2. Quickly add a few words to describe your feelings (either positive or negative) for each sentence. The lists below will help you to get started.

For example:
1. Not worrying about money
2. Honesty
3. Generosity
4. Saving as much as possible
5. Sticking to our budget

Write your own list before looking at your partner's and writing your 'agreed list'.

My list	**Our agreed list**
1. _____	1. _____
2. _____	2. _____
3. _____	3. _____
4. _____	4. _____
5. _____	5. _____

Please turn over →

EXERCISE 3 (continued)

3. Write down an area of conflict regarding money and possessions.
   Each write down any possible solutions you can think of. Then put
   your agreed solution for now.

For example:

Issue	Possible solutions	Agreed solution for now
Car keeps breaking down	• *Buy another car now* • *Spend enough money to mend the car properly* • *Change the car in 6 months* • *Use public transport* • *Find a different mechanic* • *Change the car the next time it breaks down*	*Find a different mechanic*

Issue	Possible solutions	Agreed solution for now

If your attitudes towards money and possessions rarely cause conflict
between you, move on to one of the other options in Part Two of the
exercise on 'Household Chores' (page 47), 'How You Spend Free Time'
(page 50) or 'Parenting' (page 53).

Matching Our Strides – Part Two

Household chores

1. Each of you circle the phrases that best describe your feelings (and the messages you received from your family) about money and possessions as you grew up.

• Housework shared – no traditional gender roles • Traditional roles (eg mother cooked; father did maintenance) • Employed a cleaner / other household staff	• Take turns to do chores as and when needed (relaxed approach) • Prefer to divide chores and have fixed roles • Create a chart for who does what
• Grew up in city (with no garden) • Grew up in suburbs (some outdoor work) • Grew up in country / on a farm (lots of outdoor work)	• Chores assigned in an organised manner • Children not expected to help around the house • Children responsible for many household chores
• Parent(s) did a lot of DIY projects / maintenance • Parents preferred to call contractor when things needed repair	• Grew up in neat, organised home • Grew up in messy, disorganised home
• House cleaned and tidied regularly • Allowed mess to accumulate and then cleaned	• Enjoyed helping around the house as a child • Disliked helping around the house as a child
• Confident with DIY projects • Uncomfortable with DIY	• Enjoy cooking • Do not enjoy cooking

Other significant words / phrases that describe your attitude to household chores:

Show each other what you have put and discuss any differences.

Please turn over

EXERCISE 3 (continued)

2. Our values regarding household chores (ie what is most important for us).

For example:
1. Share household chores equally
2. Make home feel 'lived in' and relaxed
3. Pay for household maintenance
4. Keep home clean and tidy
5. Limit amount of time we spend on household chores and DIY

Write your own list before looking at your partner's and writing your 'agreed list'.

My list	Our agreed list
1.	1.
2.	2.
3.	3.
4.	4.
5.	5.

EXERCISE 3 (continued)

3. Write down an area of conflict regarding money and possessions. Each write down any possible solutions you can think of. Then put your agreed solution for now.

For example:

Issue	Possible solutions	Agreed solution for now
Both husband and wife are employed full-time – who does the cleaning?	• *Do chores as needed – whoever has the time* • *Create a chart, assigning chores to each person* • *Take turns each week / weekend* • *Employ someone to clean the house* • *Do chores together at weekends* • *Assign some chores to older children*	*Create a chart to assign chores and employ a cleaner to come in once each week*

Issue	Possible solutions	Agreed solution for now

Please turn over

How You Spend Free Time

1. Each of you circle the words or phrases that best describe your feelings (and the messages you received from your family as you grew up) about how to spend free time.

• Weekends well planned • Weekends relaxed and casual • Weekends used for socialising • Weekends used to catch up on chores	• Most free time spent as a couple • Most free time spent as an individual • Most free time spent with friends and family	• Involved in many sports / activities • Hobbies / intellectual pursuits important • Not involved in many activities or sports
• Relaxing, low activity holidays • High activity holidays • Play a lot of sport on holiday	• Parents went out together frequently without children • Parents stayed at home and we had fun together as a family	• Meals eaten together as a family regularly • Everyone fended for themselves at meal times
• Preferred spending summer holidays staying with wider family • Preferred holidays spent at home	• Morning person – get up early and go to bed early • Evening person – sleep in late and stay up late	• Enjoyed having guests in our home • Preferred not having many guests in our home
• Structured and planned • Flexible and spontaneous	• Public holidays spent at home • Public holidays spent visiting family	• Spent a lot of time with extended family • Rarely saw extended family
• Ate most meals at home • Ate many meals in restaurants	• TV watched infrequently • TV a central part of family life	• Luxury travel • Budget travel

EXERCISE 3 (continued)

Other significant words / phrases that describe your attitude regarding how you like to spend your free time:

_____

_____

_____

Show each other what you have put and discuss any differences.

2. Our values regarding free time (ie what is most important to us).

    For example:
    1. Structured / planned
    2. Travelling together
    3. Mealtimes important
    4. Entertain friends in our home
    5. Time to pursue individual hobbies

Write your own list before looking at your partner's and writing your 'agreed list'.

My list	**Our agreed list**
1. _____	1. _____
2. _____	2. _____
3. _____	3. _____
4. _____	4. _____
5. _____	5. _____

Please turn over →

EXERCISE 3 (continued)

3. Write down an area of conflict regarding how you spend free time. Each write down any possible solutions you can think of. Then put your agreed solution for now.

For example:

Issue	Possible solutions	Agreed solution for now
Where to spend Christmas	• *Visit family further away* • *Divide holiday between family time and time on own* • *Host both families at home* • *Go away for Christmas* • *Choose destination / resort for families to meet together* • *Take turns each year visiting different sides of the family*	*Spend Christmas alone at home and then travel to see extended family after Christmas Day*

Issue	Possible solutions	Agreed solution for now

Parenting

1. Each of you circle the words or phrases that best describe your feelings (and the messages you received from your family) about parenting as you grew up.

• Spanking used to discipline • 'Time out', grounding and other forms of discipline used • Children allowed to do what they liked	• Regularly spent time as a family having fun together • Rarely had fun together as a family • Dreaded being together as a family	• Money invested in education • No money available to invest in education • No desire to invest in education
• Attended church and prayed together • Did not regularly attend church or pray together	• Encouraged as children to be increasingly independent • Sheltered – independence not encouraged	• Calm and quiet – disagreements avoided • Disagreements aired with much discussion and passion
• Encouraging / accepting • Performance-based and somewhat critical	• Parents very involved in children's activities • Parents not very involved in children's activities	• Encouraged to express negative emotions • Stoic and non-emotional
• Lots of affection and expressions of love • Little affection and expressions of love	• Strict / disciplinarian • Relaxed / informal • Balance of love and firm boundaries	• Allowed to watch as much TV as liked • Limited on amount of TV allowed to watch
• No arguing in front of children • A lot of arguing in front of children	• Pressure to achieve • Relaxed and allowed to find own level	

Please turn over

EXERCISE 3 (continued)

Other significant words / phrases that describe your attitude to parenting:

_____

_____

Show each other what you have put and discuss any differences.

2. Our values regarding parenting (ie what is most important for us).

For example:
1. Set clear boundaries for the children
2. Be affectionate (lots of hugs and kisses)
3. Spend regular time together as a family having fun
4. Support each other in front of the children
5. Pass on spiritual values

Write your own list before looking at your partner's and writing your 'agreed list'.

My list	**Our agreed list**
1. _____	1. _____
2. _____	2. _____
3. _____	3. _____
4. _____	4. _____
5. _____	5. _____

3. Write down an area of conflict regarding parenting. Each write down any possible solutions you can think of. Then put your agreed solution for now.

For example:

Issue	Possible solutions	Agreed solution for now
How to balance work and raising children – should mother work outside home?	• *Mother works full-time* • *Mother works part-time* • *Mother works from home* • *Mother stays at home full-time with children* • *Mother stays at home with children until they go to school* • *Father stays at home with children*	*Mother stays at home with children until they go to school and then returns to work*

Issue	Possible solutions	Agreed solution for now

Marriage Time
Session 3 – Homework

Complete Exercise 3 – 'Matching Our Strides – Part Two' on pages 47–55 if you haven't already done so and if 'Household Chores', 'How You Spend Free Time' or 'Parenting' cause conflict between you.

EXERCISE 1

Focusing on the Issue

The purpose of this exercise is to discuss any other areas of conflict and to discover the best solutions together. Make sure you are requesting rather than demanding changes in each other.

1. Each of you write down one issue that causes conflict in your marriage which arises from a habit or pattern of behaviour in you that needs to be changed.

_____

_____

_____

2. What needs to happen for you to change this pattern of behaviour?

_____

_____

_____

3. What could your partner do to help you to change?

_____

_____

_____

Now, using the 'Six Practical Steps to Peace' on page 40 as a guideline, negotiate the areas of conflict that you each identified.

4. Our agreed mutually acceptable solution is:

_____

_____

_____

5. Write down one issue that causes conflict in your marriage which arises from a habit or pattern of behaviour **in your partner** that could be changed. Be specific and positive as you raise areas of importance to you.

   For example:
   'I would love it if you could be more affectionate when we meet after work.'
   'I wish we could stop criticising each other in front of others / the children.'
   'I would really appreciate it if we could be more punctual.'

_____

_____

_____

Please turn over →

EXERCISE 1 (continued)

6. What could your partner do to change this pattern of behaviour?

_____

_____

_____

7. What could you do to help your partner to change?
(NB: personal criticism, shouting, nagging, bullying, etc are unhelpful)

_____

_____

_____

Again, using the 'Six Practical Steps to Peace' on page 40, negotiate the areas of conflict you each identified for point 5 on the previous page.

8. Our agreed mutually acceptable solution is:

_____

_____

_____

9. Would you like to spend a few minutes praying together each day? If so, when and how could this best be achieved?

_____

_____

_____

4 The Power of Forgiveness

The Power of Forgiveness

Introduction
- To say sorry and forgive is so important because we will all hurt our partner
- Dealing with hurt is vital to intimacy
- Relationships grow through trust and openness
- Hurt undermines trust and openness

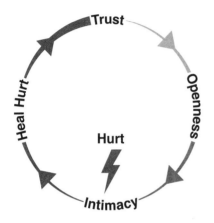

Reactions to hurt

1. Anger
- Some are like rhinos – they attack when provoked
- Some are like hedgehogs – they withdraw when threatened

Rhinos and Hedgehogs

Identify whether you are a rhino or hedgehog.
If you're not sure, ask your partner.

2. Retaliation
- To let our partner know what the hurt felt like

3. Fear
- We withdraw so as not to be hurt again

4. Guilt
- Hurt will always be caused by both partners

'In your anger do not sin. Do not let the sun go down while you are still angry, and do not give the devil a foothold.'

Ephesians 4:26–27

Notes

EXERCISE 2

Handling Anger

The purpose of this exercise is to help you recognise how each of you typically responds when you feel hurt and how you display anger.

1. Put a number between 0 and 4 in the box against each statement to indicate how true it is **for you**. Then add up columns A and B.

0. never   **1.** rarely   **2.** sometimes   **3.** often   **4.** always

When I'm hurt, I...

1. Keep the peace at any price	☐
2. Overreact and go on the attack	☐
3. Fail to admit I am angry / hurt	☐
4. Apologise because I must have caused it	☐
5. Become controlling and bossy	☐
6. Give my husband / wife the silent treatment	☐
7. Am quick to blame others	☐
8. Retaliate by becoming confrontational	☐
9. Withdraw or shut down emotionally	☐
10. Want to run away and hide	☐
11. Lose control / become explosive by shouting / slamming doors, etc	☐
12. Say things I later regret	☐
13. Try to ignore my feelings	☐
14. Become cold and clinical or sarcastic	☐
15. Say things to hurt my partner	☐
16. Withhold physical affection / sex	☐
17. Demand immediate discussion of issue	☐
18. Hurl accusations to take the focus off my responsibility	☐
19. Feel I don't have a right to be angry	☐
20. Bring up past hurt not related to the issue	☐

Totals   ☐ ☐
           A   B

	My score	Partner's score
A = Rhino Behaviour	_____	_____
B = Hedgehog Behaviour	_____	_____

EXERCISE 2 (continued)

Now look at each other's scores and discuss them, especially your differences.

2. At times of disagreement, what words or phrases are you aware that you use, if any, that hurt your partner?

_____

_____

What words or phrases does your partner use, if any, that hurt you?
(This question is especially important if either or both of you recognise that you react like the rhino.)

_____

_____

3. At times of disagreement, are you and your partner able to express your views and feelings?

_____

_____

If not, how could you help your partner to do so?
(This question is especially important if either or both of you recognise that you react like the hedgehog.)

_____

_____

What happens if hurt and anger are buried?

Physical symptoms
- Disturbed sleep
- Appetite affected
- Medical conditions, eg: ulcers, high blood pressure, pain

Behavioural symptoms
- Inability to relax
- Low sexual desire
- Quick temper / intolerance
- Escape through drugs, alcohol, pornography, etc
- Escape into work / children / religious activities etc

Emotional symptoms
- Loss of positive emotions, eg: romance, love, joy
- Low self-esteem / depression
- Shut down
- Fear of confrontation

Process for healing hurt

1. Identify the hurt
- Take the initiative to resolve anger and heal hurt
- Recognise the ways in which you have caused pain to your partner and hurt your marriage (see Matthew 5:23–24)
- Be prepared to tell your partner when you have been hurt (see Matthew 18:15)

'Therefore, if you are offering your gift at the altar and there remember that your brother or sister has something against you, leave your gift there in front of the altar. First go and be reconciled to them; then come and offer your gift.'

Matthew 5:23–24

2. Apologise

- Take responsibility
- Resist the urge to make excuses or to blame your partner
- Confess to God and receive forgiveness
- Enables us to see the effect of our actions
- Apologise to each other
- Opens the way for reconciliation and healing

'If your brother or sister sins against you, go and show them their fault, just between the two of you. If they listen to you, you have won them over.'

Matthew 18:15

EXERCISE 3

Identifying Unresolved Hurt

This exercise concentrates particularly on identifying the areas of hurt and seeking to understand each other's feelings better. The homework focuses on apology and forgiveness.

Try to identify your partner's hurt

Think about ways in which you have hurt your partner and affected your marriage that have not been resolved between you. Think back to when you were going out, when you were engaged and early times in your marriage, as well as recent times. (None of us is perfect.)

- What have I failed to do that I should be doing?
- What have I done (or am I doing) that I should not do?
- Where have I failed to meet my husband's / wife's needs?
- What have I said that has been hurtful?
- What have I left unsaid that could have shown love and encouragement?

Don't make excuses or blame your partner. The following examples show the difference:

Making excuses / blaming our partner:

'I know I criticised you in front of the children yesterday, but I wouldn't have done so if you hadn't made us twenty minutes late.'

Please turn over →

Proper apology:
'I hurt you by criticising you in front of the children yesterday; it was unkind of me. I am sorry.'

Making excuses / blaming our partner:
'I know I was grumpy and rude towards you last night, but you don't understand what intense pressure I've been under at work for the last two weeks.'

Proper apology:
'It was selfish and insensitive of me to be rude and grumpy towards you last night. I am sorry to have hurt you.'

Write a list of the things that come to mind. Be specific.

(**For example:** *'I have stopped being affectionate and rejected your initiatives to make love; I have fallen asleep in front of the television instead of talking with you; I have been out more consistently with work colleagues or friends than we have together as a couple; I said some very unkind things during that big argument we had two weeks ago about money.'*)

_____

_____

_____

_____

_____

Identify your own hurt

Identify the ways in which you have been hurt by your partner. The cause of the hurt could be recent or a long time ago. Your partner might or might not have been aware of hurting you and it could have been one incident or repeated many times. Make sure you are specific and that you describe how you felt. Use 'I' sentences.

EXERCISE 3 (continued)

(For example: 'I felt unsupported and unappreciated when you didn't notice the hard work I put into decorating the house for Christmas; I was hurt when you didn't say anything special about my promotion; I haven't got over the fact that you lied to me on the night we first went out together; I felt rejected when you went out to the pub the night we got back from our honeymoon; I feel frustrated because you don't discuss financial decisions with me.')

_____

_____

_____

_____

_____

1. When you have both finished, exchange your lists.

2. Read silently the ways you have hurt each other.

3. One of you then 'reflect back' to your partner the reason for their hurt and the feelings it produced in them, without trying to interpret what they have written or to defend yourself. To clarify what they feel, ask questions such as: 'What did you mean by that?' or 'Is there anything else you would like to say?'

4. Then the other partner should 'reflect back' in the same way. Make sure each of you has an understanding of the feelings that are described.

5. Return the lists to each other. Then add to or revise your list of the ways you have hurt your partner. Spend some time considering every aspect of their hurt. Try to see it through your partner's eyes.

6. Throughout the coming week, allow God the opportunity to show you new insights into why your partner feels hurt and your part in causing it.

7. It is important to do the homework in order to complete the process of 'getting rid of bitterness, rage and anger' (Ephesians 4:31) by apologising and forgiving.

3. Forgive

- Forgiveness is essential and one of the greatest forces for healing in a marriage
- Degrees of difficulty in forgiving
- Jesus on the cross of those who crucified him
- Small issues, eg: husband or wife forgetting to do something or making you late
- Big issues, eg: unfaithfulness
- Forgiveness is, first and foremost, a choice, not a feeling
- Question is not, 'Do we feel like forgiving?'
- Question is, 'Will we forgive? Will we let go of our self-pity / demand for justice / desire to retaliate?'

'Father, forgive them for they know not what they do.'

Luke 23:34

Forgiveness IS NOT

- Demanding a person changes before we forgive them
- Pretending it doesn't matter and trying to forget about it
- Thinking time alone will heal the hurt

Forgiveness IS

- Facing the wrong done to us
- Recognising the emotions inside
- Releasing the other person into God's hands, leaving the consequences to him
- Choosing not to hold it against our husband or wife
- If we do not forgive we'll be the one imprisoned by the bitterness, resentment, and anger
- Forgiveness is a process – we often need to keep forgiving for the same hurt – sometimes on a daily basis
- God forgives us freely and therefore we must forgive each other freely

'Get rid of all bitterness, rage and anger... Be kind and compassionate to one another, forgiving each other, just as in Christ God forgave you.'

Ephesians 4:31–32

Start again together

- Begin each day with a fresh start and no backlog – tear off each page of the notebook
- Don't expect healing to be instant – apology and forgiveness remove the distance between us but the hurt leaves a bruising that needs time to heal
- Re-build trust by setting aside marriage time, and being gentle and kind towards each other
- Pray for one another – pray aloud or silently, asking God to heal your partner of the hurt you have caused him or her

This process is like a drain that carries away the hurt. Confession to God and those we hurt, together with forgiving those who have hurt us, must become a daily habit if intimacy is to be maintained. Otherwise the drain begins to block up with unresolved hurt and anger.

'Peter came to Jesus and asked, "Lord, how many times shall I forgive my brother or sister when they sin against me? Up to seven times?" Jesus answered, "I tell you, not seven times but seventy times seven."'

Matthew 18:21–22

'Love keeps no record of wrongs.'

1 Corinthians 13:5

'Forgetting what lies behind and pressing forward to what lies ahead.'

Philippians 3:13

Supporting Each Other

Ask your husband or wife to tell you one way that you can support them this week. If you feel comfortable, pray for each other – aloud or silently. Otherwise express your support in some other way.

'Confess your faults to one another and pray for one another that you may be healed.'

James 5:16

Marriage Time
Session 4 – Homework

If you have not done so, finish the exercise 'Identifying Unresolved Hurt' on pages 65–67 and exchange lists as described on page 67.

Make sure you have at least two hours alone for marriage time this week.

on pages 65–67 and exchange lists as described on page 67.

EXERCISE 1

Healing Unresolved Hurt

Do steps 1–4 on your own and then do steps 5–8 together.

1. Identify your partner's deepest hurt

Refer back to your list of your partner's hurts on page 66 and write down here the principal way in which you know you have hurt your husband / wife.
(For example: 'I hurt my husband / wife through making a joke about the misunderstanding between us; my husband / wife was hurt when I paid more attention to my work than to him / her.')

One of the principal ways I have hurt my husband / wife is:

_____

_____

_____

2. Try to understand your partner's feelings

With regard to this hurt, my husband / wife feels:

(For example: ridiculed, humiliated, unaffirmed, criticised, rejected, unloved, undervalued.)

_____

_____

_____

3. Recognise your responsibility (refuse to make excuses or to blame your husband or wife)

- *'I did it'*
- *'It was wrong'*
- *'I need to be forgiven by God and by my husband / wife'*
- *'I need to be prepared to change'*

From now on, with God's help, I intend to:

_____

_____

_____

Now repeat steps 1–3 with any other ways you have hurt your husband / wife.

> '... now I am happy, not because you were made sorry, but because your sorrow led you to repentance. For you became sorrowful as God intended and so were not harmed in any way by us.'
>
> 2 Corinthians 7:9

Please turn over →

EXERCISE 1 (continued)

4. Confess your sins to God

- Be specific – *'Lord God, I have hurt you and my husband / wife by:*

_____

_____

_____

'This was wrong and I ask you to forgive me. Thank you for taking my guilt on the cross and for giving me a new start. I ask you to help me to be the husband / wife you want me to be.'

Believe God's promise of forgiveness and cleansing.

> 'If we confess our sins, he is faithful and just and will forgive us our sins and purify us from all unrighteousness.'
>
> 1 John 1:9

5. Say sorry to each other

'I am so sorry for: _____

_____

_____

I know it hurts you and makes you feel: _____

_____

_____

From now on I intend to: _____

_____

Please forgive me.'

EXERCISE 1 (continued)

6. Forgive each other

- Say to your husband / wife, *'I forgive you'*
- For some people this is a struggle; it can be helpful first to express to God in writing our desire to forgive our husband / wife for particular hurts:

For example:
Dear Lord, thank you that you know all about me and love me. Thank you for being ready to forgive me for the ways I have hurt others. You know how hurt and angry I felt when my husband / wife criticised me when I'd done my best. I choose to let go of my anger and resentment. I want to put my desire to retaliate into your hands, and ask you to help my husband / wife to change. I choose to forgive him / her as you have forgiven me. Please heal the hurt with your love.

> 'Forgive us our trespasses as we forgive those who trespass against us.'
>
> Luke 11:4

7. Comfort and pray for each other

- This is very valuable when you have made yourselves vulnerable to each other
- This brings healing to the hurt
- Pray that your husband / wife will know freedom from guilt

8. Do something you both enjoy together

- In this way you will start to replace the negative emotions with positive ones

The Impact of Family – Past and Present

5

The Impact of Family – Past and Present

Introduction
- Family background has a big influence on a marriage
- The expectations of different generations can cause tension within the wider family
- We either repeat or react against the way our parents behaved, particularly when we are relaxed or stressed
  - the positive – be grateful for what was good in your own and your husband or wife's upbringing
  - the different – recognise each other's different expectations of family traditions and husband / wife roles and work out *your* way of doing things
  - the negative – difficult relationships with our wider family, or childhood pain can put a strain on our marriage – it's important to address these issues so we can understand each other and move forward as a couple

Notes

Stages of growing up

1. Early years

Our parents' role:

- To meet our physical and emotional needs
- To set appropriate boundaries
- To show unconditional love
- To provide a role model of a good marriage

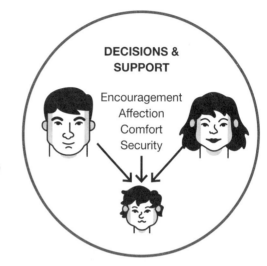

2. Teenage years

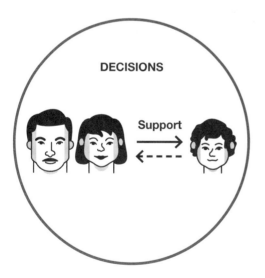

Our parents' role:

- To give increasing independence
- To continue to meet our physical and emotional needs and set boundaries
- To show unconditional love
- To teach us to consider their needs and to start to give something back

3. Coming of age / leaving home

Our parents' role:

- To give support and advice (we may still have looked to our parental home for advice, comfort, money or help with the laundry)
- To allow independence and encourage us to make our own decisions
- To make the transition to an adult relationship

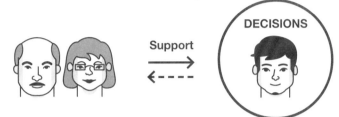

4. Getting married

As a married couple, the independence must be complete:

- A new centre of gravity
- Establish your own home as a new decision-making structure
- Seek to meet each other's needs
- Develop a relationship of mutual support with parents and parents-in-law
- Put in place boundaries, not to cut you off from parents, but to connect as a couple with them in a new way

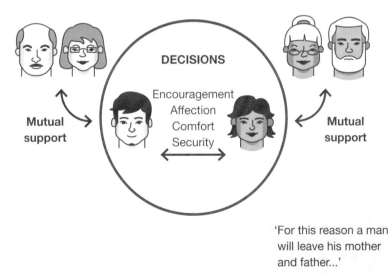

'For this reason a man will leave his mother and father...'

Genesis 2:24

Current Relationships

Talk about your current relationships with wider family members and see if you can identify anything that's causing tension.

Building healthy family relationships

1. Resolve any conflict

- All relationships involve some conflict
- Identify the issue causing tension and consider discussing it with parents / in-laws
- Apologise when you have been wrong
- Choose to forgive and move on

'As far as it depends on you live at peace with everyone.'

Romans 12:18

2. Consider their needs

- Show gratitude to your parents
- Don't abuse their availability
- Maintain contact
- Take the initiative to telephone regularly, visit, enable them to see their grandchildren, etc
- Give support
  - offer advice when needed
  - give practical help
  - consider living nearby / together

'Honour your father and your mother...'

Exodus 20:12

3. Make our own decisions
- Listen to parents' advice
- Never decide on an important issue with parents without discussing it together first
- Agree on your policy and stand together
- Do not give away the ups and downs of your relationship
- Supporting each other increases your emotional closeness

EXERCISE 2

Building Healthy Family Relationships

Look at the three principles above for building healthy relationships with your wider family, and discuss which points are most relevant for you.

Looking at our past
- Negative experiences from our past can affect the way we react to our partner
- There may be buried hurt and anger that comes out against our husband / wife
- Recognise childhood needs that were not met during your upbringing and any buried hurt and anger
- Adult relationships require us to accept our parents as they are / were rather than as we would like them to be / to have been

Notes

Reflect on Your Upbringing

A. Your immediate family relationships

- The big circle drawn below represents yourself
- Use coins to represent members of your immediate family

1. Each of you spend three or four minutes arranging the coins according to the closeness of the relationships between your immediate family as you were growing up, where:

- **Coins touching** = relationship
  (ie, together with some communication)

- **Coins overlapping** = close relationship
  (ie, good, open communication and conflict well resolved)

- **Coins separate** = lack of relationship
  (ie, divorced, separated or no communication)

2. Draw around them marking in the names.

3. Look at each other's arrangement.

For example:

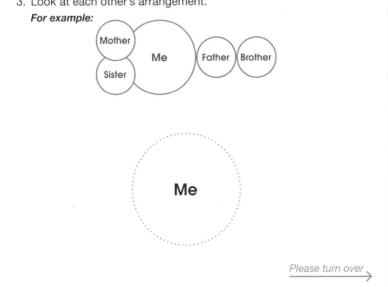

Please turn over

B. Your parents' / step-parents' (or whoever brought you up) relationship with you

Please consider the following questions and tick the relevant boxes:

Did your parents or step-parents...	Mother/ Step-mother (✓ tick if Yes)	Father/ Step-father (✓ tick if Yes)
praise you as a child?	☐	☐
meet your physical needs (for food, clothes, home, etc)?	☐	☐
give you a sense of security?	☐	☐
respect your uniqueness?	☐	☐
encourage you in your development?	☐	☐
set clear rules / appropriate boundaries for you?	☐	☐
give you increasing freedom appropriate to your age?	☐	☐
comfort you when you were upset?	☐	☐
give you presents?	☐	☐
take an interest in your life?	☐	☐
treat their children equally?	☐	☐
admit their mistakes and apologise when necessary?	☐	☐
forgive you for your mistakes?	☐	☐
have realistic expectations of what was appropriate for your age?	☐	☐
accept your friends?	☐	☐
help you relate well to your siblings and peers?	☐	☐
establish clear family rules?	☐	☐
give discipline in a consistent, fair way?	☐	☐
spend ample time with you (ie, play with you, talk to you, etc)?	☐	☐
show you physical affection (ie, hug you, kiss you, etc)?	☐	☐

C. Your parents' / step-parents' (or whoever brought you up) relationship with each other

Did your parents or step-parents...	Yes	Sometimes	No	Don't know
have a strong loving relationship?	☐	☐	☐	☐
show interest in each other?	☐	☐	☐	☐
have fun together regularly?	☐	☐	☐	☐
spend time together on their own?	☐	☐	☐	☐
show each other physical affection?	☐	☐	☐	☐
help each other in small or big tasks?	☐	☐	☐	☐
encourage each other with praise and appreciation?	☐	☐	☐	☐
show each other respect?	☐	☐	☐	☐
communicate honestly and directly?	☐	☐	☐	☐
listen to each other without interrupting or criticising?	☐	☐	☐	☐
resolve conflicts effectively?	☐	☐	☐	☐
apologise to and forgive each other when appropriate?	☐	☐	☐	☐
agree on the use of their money?	☐	☐	☐	☐
give each other presents?	☐	☐	☐	☐
have mutual interests?	☐	☐	☐	☐
show a willingness to negotiate?	☐	☐	☐	☐
remain faithful to each other?	☐	☐	☐	☐

When you've finished A, B and C above, please discuss the following questions together:

- What do you need to be grateful for from your upbringing?
- Did you have any unmet childhood needs?
- Are you aware of these adversely affecting your marriage?
- Are you aware of benefits to your marriage / family life through imitating your parents / step-parents / main caregivers?
- Are you aware of ways you adversely affect your marriage / family life through imitating your parents / step-parents / main caregivers?

Healing childhood pain

1. Recognise unmet childhood needs
- Do not be surprised if you encounter strong feelings as you do this
- Give God permission to open your heart and express your feelings to him

2. Grieve with each other
- Allow your husband or wife to talk about what has been lost and give him / her emotional support
- Receive comfort from your partner but do not demand it

'Rejoice with those who rejoice; mourn with those who mourn.'

Romans 12:15

3. Forgive
- Give up any desire to repay
- Give up continuing expectations and longings of what you have wanted your parents or others to be for you
- Remember forgiveness is an ongoing act of the will and is essential for healing

4. Look to God and move on
- Nothing is beyond God's power to heal and restore
- Pray for yourself and each other
- Ask God to heal the sense of loss and to help you to know his love
- Dwell on the promises of God in the Bible
- Believe God's unconditional love for you as you are now
- Do not use childhood pain as an excuse for not meeting your partner's needs

'I have loved you with an everlasting love and am constant in my affection for you.'

Jeremiah 31:3

Supporting each other
Ask your husband or wife if there's one thing they're concerned about at the moment. Then, if you're comfortable praying, pray for each other. Otherwise, express your support in some other way.

Marriage Time
Session 5 – Homework

EXERCISE 1

Relating to Parents

A. Being aware of the past
Spend 10 minutes filling in your 'Life Graph' overleaf (example below).

- Record the most significant events that come to mind
- Put positive experiences above the 'neutral line', between 0 and +100
- Put negative experiences below the 'neutral line', between 0 and –100
- Show your husband or wife what you have put
- Consider whether you have been able to forgive those who have hurt you
- Tell your husband or wife what you felt then and what you feel now about these events
- Where one of you has been hurt by others during your upbringing, check that you are both going through the four steps for 'Healing childhood pain' (page 84)

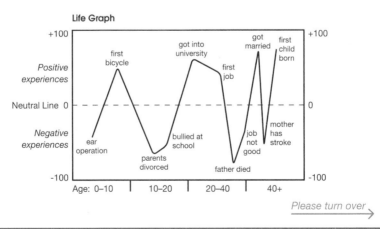

Life Graph

Please turn over →

Life Graph

+100

Positive experiences

Neutral line 0 –

Negative experiences

-100

Age: 0–10   10–20

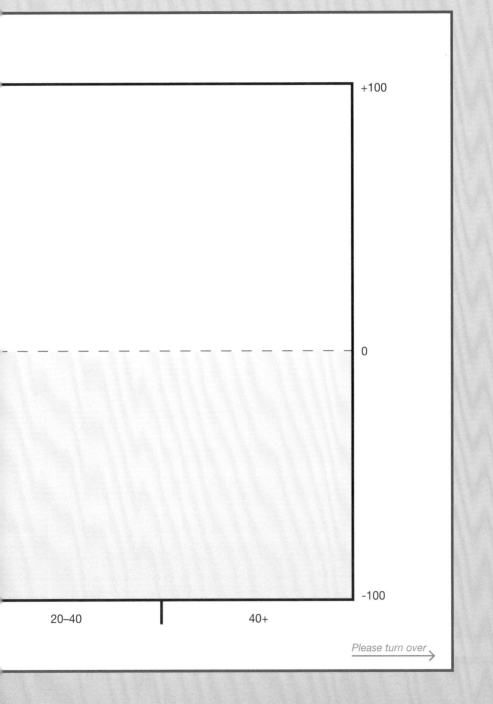

+100

0

-100

20–40   40+

Please turn over →

B. Supporting each other

Each of you should fill in the following questions on your own, and then exchange your answers. Please consider carefully what your partner has written. Discuss the significant issues – pay particular attention to an issue that your partner has highlighted and you have not. You may need to adjust some of your own answers as a result.

1. Do your parents (seek to) control or interfere in your decisions and the direction of your lives? If so, specify the ways.

_____

_____

_____

_____

2. Is there an unhealthy emotional dependence between you and a parent, or your partner and a parent? If so, in what way?

_____

_____

_____

_____

EXERCISE 1 (continued)

3. Are there issues relating to your parents (in-law) that cause tension or arguments between you?

For example:
'There is often tension between us when I have spent a long time on the telephone with one of my parents.'

_____

_____

_____

_____

4. In what way could you support your partner with regard to your parents and in-laws?

_____

_____

_____

_____

5. In what way could your partner support you with regard to your parents and in-laws?

_____

_____

_____

_____

Please turn over →

EXERCISE 1 (continued)

6. a) Do you or your partner have unmet childhood needs?
   If so, how could you help your partner?

_____

_____

_____

b) How could your partner help you?

_____

_____

_____

C. Supporting your parents

1. How could you express your gratitude towards your parents (and / or parents-in-law)?

_____

_____

_____

2. How can you best keep in touch with your parents (and/or parents-in-law)? Consider telephone calls, timing and length of visits, and other ways of communicating with them.

_____

_____

_____

EXERCISE 1 (continued)

3. Consider the needs of your parents and parents-in-law. From the list below, tick the relevant boxes for the needs of both your parents and parents-in-law. Beside the boxes you have ticked, write the ways you could help meet those needs.

Husband's parent(s)	Needs	Wife's parent(s)
☐	Advice	☐
☐	Companionship	☐
☐	Conversation	☐
☐	Encouragement	☐
☐	Practical help	☐
☐	Security	☐
☐	Understanding	☐
☐	*Other need*	☐
☐	*Other need*	☐

6 Good Sex

Building Strong Foundations

- Make marriage time a weekly priority in your diaries
- Discover and seek to meet your partner's needs (see 'Knowing Me, Knowing You', page 14)

The Art of Communication

- Talk about your feelings with your partner this week
- Listen to your partner's feelings without interrupting, criticising or offering advice

Resolving Conflict

- Express your appreciation for your partner every day
- When you disagree, discuss the issue rather than attack each other
- Spend a few minutes each day praying with and for each other, or show your support in another way

The Power of Forgiveness

- Keep 'the drain' clear of unresolved hurt and anger
- Identify, apologise for and forgive the ways you have hurt each other

Good Sex

Notes

Introduction

How we view sex makes all the difference.

1. Our consumer society

- Sex largely separated from relationship and commitment
- Desire for instant gratification
- Assumption that good sex can only be found in a new relationship or an affair

2. A way of developing intimacy

- A gift from God for our pleasure and enjoyment within marriage (see, for example, Song of Songs in the Bible)
- A way of communicating love that goes beyond words
- Expresses and deepens the 'one flesh' bond
- Potential for growth of sexual relationship
- Designed to develop over a lifetime as mutual love and understanding grow

'I am my lover's and my lover is mine...'

Song of Songs 6:3

3. A vital part of a strong and healthy marriage

- Not the icing on the cake but a vital ingredient of the cake itself
- Not to be compartmentalised
- Sexual intimacy affects every other part of our marriage and vice versa
- Often the first casualty to tiredness or laziness
- May need to make lifestyle changes eg, increase exercise, change eating habits

4. Problems can be worked through

- Most couples struggle with their sexual relationship at one time or another
- Sexual desire can and must be reawakened
- Don't regard as 'your' issue or 'my' issue but 'our' issue
- Most problems resolved through better understanding and making changes
- Some involve deeper issues from the past – can be healed and restored through prayer and professional help

Six qualities for great lovers

1. The importance of communication

- Difficult at first because deeply private and requires vulnerability
- Enables us to understand each other better and increases our intimacy
- Differences between male and female sexuality – men tend to think about the destination; women tend to think about the journey
- Tell each other what you enjoy – don't leave to guesswork
- Takes courage and trust to bring fears out into the open
- Storing up negative emotions is often a barrier to sexual enjoyment

> **EXERCISE 1**
>
> Ask your partner what is most relevant for them so far in this session.

2. The importance of tenderness

- Take time over lovemaking
- Focus on giving to one another
- Tune in to each other's emotional needs and resolve conflict first
- Increase non-sexual touching – holding hands, arm around a shoulder, etc
- Never criticise your spouse's natural shape – instead tell each other what you love about each other's body

'His left arm is under my head, and his right arm embraces me.'

Song of Songs 2:6

Notes

3. The importance of responsiveness

- Responding sexually can give our partner a sense of confidence and well-being
- Sex often starts as a decision and then arousal follows
- Giving ourselves sexually requires a climate of trust
- Trust can be rebuilt over time through choosing to forgive

4. The importance of romance

- Creates the setting for lovemaking
- The antidote to mechanical and routine sex
- Learn the art of seduction and arousal
- Take the initiative

Lover: 'You are a garden locked up... my bride you are a spring enclosed, a sealed fountain.'

Beloved: 'Awake, north wind, and come, south wind! Blow on my garden, that its fragrance may spread abroad. Let my lover come into his garden and taste its choice fruits.'

Song of Songs 4:12 & 16

EXERCISE 2

Tell each other what have been the most romantic moments for you in your relationship.

---

5. The importance of anticipation

- Our mind is our most important sexual asset
- Communicate your desire – the best sex starts at breakfast
- Mutually agreed periods of sexual abstinence can enhance a couple's sexual relationship
- Be sure sexual thoughts and desires are directed towards partner
- The dangers of pornography
- Fantasising about our spouse is healthy

Visit **themarriagecourse.org** for information on where to find help for issues with pornography.

'Finally, brothers and sisters, whatever is true, whatever is noble, whatever is right, whatever is pure, whatever is lovely, whatever is admirable – if anything is excellent or praiseworthy – think about such things.'

Philippians 4:8

6. The importance of variety

- Familiarity often breeds complacency
- Creativity and romance produce excitement
- Make love in different settings
- Vary the time – last thing at night is not always the best time
- Vary the atmosphere – soft lighting can help
- Vary the routine – read a book about building a good sexual relationship together

'... at our door is every delicacy, both new and old, that I have stored up for you, my lover.'

Song of Songs 7:13

40% of women and 30% of men will experience a sexual problem at some point. Visit **themarriagecourse.org** for a list of recommended books for building a good sexual relationship.

EXCERCISE 3

Talking About Sex

A. Rate your lovemaking

Against the list of six qualities below, circle the number against each
category – for yourself (A) and for your husband or wife (B) – which you
feel best describes your sexual relationship, where 1 = not so good and
5 = very good:

A. You					Qualities	B. Your partner				
1	2	3	4	5	Communication	1	2	3	4	5
1	2	3	4	5	Tenderness	1	2	3	4	5
1	2	3	4	5	Responsiveness	1	2	3	4	5
1	2	3	4	5	Romance	1	2	3	4	5
1	2	3	4	5	Anticipation	1	2	3	4	5
1	2	3	4	5	Variety	1	2	3	4	5

Which area(s) do you need to work on?

_____

_____

_____

EXERCISE 3 (continued)

B. Identify problem areas

1. What, if any, are the differences between you, as husband and wife, in the way you respond sexually?

_____

Are these differences having a positive or negative effect on your marriage?

_____

If positive, give the main reason:

_____

If negative, give the main reason:

_____

2. Does your self-esteem and body image affect your lovemaking negatively?

_____

If so, explain why:

_____

_____

How could your husband or wife help you?

_____

_____

Please turn over →

EXERCISE 3 (continued)

3. What, if any, unresolved emotions (*eg: resentment, hurt, unforgiveness, anxiety or guilt*) affect your lovemaking in any way?

_____

If so, how?

_____

_____

How could these be resolved?

_____

_____

4. Does your lovemaking lack excitement?

_____

If so, what new element would you like to see introduced?

_____

_____

5. Does over-tiredness take a toll on the frequency of your lovemaking?

_____

If so, identify the reason for over-tiredness:

_____

_____

EXERCISE 3 (continued)

What could re-energise you? *(eg: exercise, better communication, resolving past hurt, planning and prioritising sex, more sleep, less going out, more fun and less work)*

_____

_____

6. Do you feel free to talk together about your lovemaking?

_____

If the answer is yes, write down two or three things your husband or wife has told you recently that have enhanced your lovemaking:

_____

_____

If the answer is no, identify some of the reasons for your difficulty:

_____

_____

Suggest something you would like your husband or wife to say that you have never heard:

_____

_____

Please turn over

C. Write the script

List below the different criteria that would create good lovemaking for you.

Be specific about things such as timing, taking the initiative, anticipation, position, atmosphere, place, romance, tenderness, seduction and arousal (foreplay), afterwards. (We cannot guess each other's expectations.)

1. _____   6. _____

2. _____   7. _____

3. _____   8. _____

4. _____   9. _____

5. _____   10. _____

D. Seek to understand each other better

- Once you have finished, read each other's responses to sections A, B and C

- Now start to talk about what the other has expressed – beginning where you feel most comfortable

- Give each other the opportunity to ask questions about what you have written. Tell your husband or wife what surprised you most. Ask for clarification if you do not fully understand

Protecting our marriage

None of us is exempt from being attracted to other people.

1. Build each other up
- Most common cause of affairs is a failure to meet each other's emotional needs

2. Set boundaries
- Infidelity starts and stops in the mind
- Avoid intimate conversations with the opposite sex
- Can't help being attracted but we can decide whether or not to entertain such thoughts
- Physical adultery is usually preceded by emotional adultery

3. Talk to someone about the feelings
- The effects of secrecy
- If feelings become overwhelming, tell your partner or someone else – this can help burst the bubble

4. Keep sex alive
- Different levels of desire
- Loving involves giving to each other – sometimes making an effort; sometimes showing restraint
- As we increase emotional intimacy, physical desire usually increases
- May need to apologise or express forgiveness to each other
- Sometimes need go back to the basics of enjoying touching and being touched

'So guard yourself in your spirit and do not break faith.'

Malachi 2:16

'I tell you that anyone who looks at a woman lustfully has already committed adultery with her in his heart.'

Matthew 5:28

'Place me like a seal over your heart, like a seal on your arm; for love is as strong as death, its jealousy unyielding as the grave. It burns like blazing fire, like a mighty flame. Many waters cannot quench love; rivers cannot wash it away. If one were to give all the wealth of one's house for love it would be utterly scorned.'

Song of Songs 8:6–7

Supporting each other
Say sorry to each other for any ways you've spoilt your sexual intimacy. Express forgiveness. Ask your partner how you can support them this week. If you feel comfortable, pray for each other, aloud or silently.

Marriage Time
Session 6 – Homework

Happiness and fulfilment in this area of our marriage will depend on meeting our husband or wife's needs, as we would like them to meet ours. Be careful not to push your partner to fulfil your desires – look to meet theirs.

Plan times of making love (even if it seems contrived at first) to fulfil what you both feel comfortable with from Section C of the exercise 'Talking About Sex' (page 102).

Love in Action

REMINDER

The aim of The Marriage Course is to establish patterns of relating that will help couples become closer and keep their marriages growing over a lifetime.

Building Strong Foundations

- Make marriage time a weekly priority in your diaries
- Discover and seek to meet your partner's needs (see 'Knowing Me, Knowing You', page 14)

The Art of Communication

- Talk about your feelings with your partner this week
- Listen to your partner's feelings without interrupting, criticising or offering advice

Resolving Conflict

- Express your appreciation for your partner every day
- When you disagree, discuss the issue rather than attack each other
- Spend a few minutes each day praying with and for each other, or show your support in another way

The Power of Forgiveness

- Keep 'the drain' clear of unresolved hurt and anger
- Identify, apologise for and forgive the ways you have hurt each other

Impact of Family – Past and Present

- Be sure you have left your parents – together make your own decisions and support each other
- Let go of unresolved hurt and anger from your upbringing through forgiveness and prayer
- Build the best possible relationships with your parents, in-laws and wider families through resolving conflict and thinking about their needs

Good Sex

- Tell each other what you enjoy – don't leave it to guess work
- Seek to meet your partner's desires rather than your own
- Don't bury problems – talk about them and seek help if necessary

Love in Action

Introduction
- Love is about more than feelings, it's about what we do –
  it involves action
- Love always means making a sacrifice for the sake of another

Five ways to express love
1. **Loving words**
2. **Thoughtful presents**
3. **Physical affection**
4. **Quality time**
5. **Kind actions**

- These expressions are like languages that communicate love
- For each of us one of these 'love languages' will
  communicate love more effectively than the others
- Most people have different love languages to their partner
- Common to try to communicate love in the way we
  understand it and want to receive it
- Learn which expressions of love are most important to your
  partner and practise using

1. Loving words
Words have great power either to build up or to undermine
our partner.

- Show appreciation for each other daily
- Give compliments and encourage each other
- Speak kindly to each other
- Make requests, not demands
- For some, hearing words of affirmation feels like arriving at
  an oasis in a desert

2. Thoughtful presents

Presents are visual symbols of love. This expression of love is the easiest to learn but we may need to change our attitude to money.

Giving presents is a way of investing in our marriage.

- Can be inexpensive but have high value (a single flower, a bar of chocolate)
- Don't wait only for special occasions
- Actively discover what your partner likes (within your budget!)

'Pleasant words are a honeycomb, sweet to the soul and healing to the bones.'

Proverbs 16:24

EXERCISE 1

Favourite Presents

Tell your partner what have been the best presents you've received from them.

Notes

3. Physical affection

Touch is a powerful communicator of love in marriage. If this is your partner's primary way of feeling loved, in times of crisis, touch will communicate more than anything else that you care.

- Touch can speak louder than words
- Takes many different forms, eg: holding hands, putting an arm round each other's shoulder or waist, a kiss, a hug, a hand on a hand, a back massage, sexual foreplay, making love
- Both sexual and non-sexual touch are important in marriage
- For many wives, touch and signs of affection have little to do with sex
- Learn how to show physical affection if it's unnatural to you

'To touch my body is to touch me. To withdraw from my body is to distance yourself from me emotionally.'

Gary Chapman

4. Quality time

Married couples can spend a lot of time together without using it to convey love to each other. Togetherness means more than physical proximity – it involves focusing our attention on our partner.

Quality time together builds friendship through:

1. Talking together
- Sharing our thoughts, feelings, hopes, fears and disappointments
- Some must learn to listen while others must learn to talk

2. Eating together
- Mealtimes are valuable opportunities for communicating on a regular basis
- Make the effort to initiate conversation
- Ask questions that the other will enjoy answering

3. Having fun together
- Friendship is built around shared experiences and shared memories
- We all need fresh experiences to breathe fresh life into our relationship

Times Together

Each write a list of what you have most enjoyed doing together in the past or perhaps would like to start doing together:

- _____

- _____

- _____

- _____

- _____

Show each other what you have put. Use your lists as ideas when planning your marriage time.

5. Kind actions

This involves expressing love through serving our husband or wife, through seeking to meet their needs in practical ways.

- Routine acts of service – meeting regular needs
- Non-routine – responding to a particular need at a particular time
- Help may be requested but should not be demanded nor taken for granted
- Ask our partner, 'Is there something I can do to help you?'

'Do to others as you would have them do to you.'

Luke 6:31

Notes

Learning to love

Jesus Christ showed love in all five ways:

1. Words
'As the Father has loved me, so have I loved you.'

John 15:9

2. Time
'Come with me by yourselves to a quiet place.'

Mark 6:31

3. Actions
'He poured some water into a basin and began to wash his disciples' feet.'

John 13:5

4. Touch
'Jesus reached out his hand and touched the man.'

Luke 5:13

5. Presents
'Jesus took the loaves, gave thanks, and distributed to those who were seated as much as they wanted.'

John 6:11

Love is not just a feeling – it requires an act of the will to meet each other's needs. We are called to imitate and obey Jesus.

'My command is this: love each other as I have loved you.'

John 15:12

Discovering Your Own and Your Partner's Love Languages

Please do questions 1 and 2 on your own and share your responses before filling in questions 4 and 5.

1. Write down up to 12 specific occasions through which you have known your partner's love for you. (It could be at any stage in your relationship – before or after marriage. These may be regular or rare events and could be deemed of major or minor significance.)

   I have known your love for me when:

   For example:
   'We sat under the stars talking about our future when we were going out.'
   'You gave me that watch on our wedding anniversary.'
   'You cooked a special meal for my birthday.'
   'You said how proud you were of me when I was promoted.'
   'You spontaneously put your arm around me when we were waiting for the film to start.'

- _____
- _____
- _____
- _____
- _____
- _____
- _____
- _____

Please turn over →

EXERCISE 3 (continued)

2. Taking into consideration your answers to question 1, put the five ways of showing love in order of importance for you, where 1 = most important and 5 = least important. Then consider in which order of importance you think they come for your partner.

For you (number 1–5)	Love languages	For your partner (number 1–5)
	Loving words	
	Thoughtful presents	
	Physical affection	
	Quality time	
	Kind actions	

3. Now, compare and discuss with your husband or wife what each of you put for questions 1 and 2.

4. Looking at your partner's first 'love language' (ie, the most important), list three ways in which you could communicate love to your husband or wife this week or this month. (Try to keep within the bounds of reality!)

1. _____

2. _____

3. _____

EXERCISE 3 (continued)

5. Looking at your partner's second 'love language' (ie, the second most important), list three more ways in which you could communicate love to your husband or wife effectively this week or this month.

   1. _____

   2. _____

   3. _____

6. Experiment and see what the results are!

*'Love does not consist of gazing at
each other, but in looking together
in the same direction.'*

Antoine de St Exupéry

Conclusion

- Marriage isn't static; it's designed to be a dynamic relationship that keeps changing
- It is a mistake to think we sort our marriage out and that's it
- Marriage is a journey
- Expressing our commitment to each other is essential to the success of the journey
- Commitment is liberating as it means we can take a long view, we can plan our future together and we can look beyond current frustrations
- When we're both committed, there's nothing we can't work through together
- We believe God has called each of us to a partnership with our husband or wife – that he wants to use

Supporting Each Other
*Ask your partner how you could best
support them regarding the future. If you feel
comfortable, say a prayer for each other, aloud
or silently. Otherwise express your support
in some other way.*

Marriage Time
Session 7 – Homework

EXERCISE 1

Putting the Course into Practice

1. Five things I especially want to remember and practise from The Marriage Course:

   1. _____

   2. _____

   3. _____

   4. _____

   5. _____

   Show your husband or wife what you have written.

2. Now ask him / her, 'What five things would you especially like me to remember and practise from The Marriage Course?' Write them below:

   1. _____

   2. _____

   3. _____

   4. _____

   5. _____

Coping With Times of Separation

Extra session for those in the Armed Forces
(and other couples required to spend time apart)

Aim of this session

To help couples become better prepared to handle times apart, and so have a marriage that grows and is strengthened through this experience.

EXERCISE 1

The Effects of Separation on Your Marriage

Discuss how involuntary separation has affected your marriage in the past, or how you think it might impact you when it happens.

Emotional cycle of deployment[1]

Stage 1: Anticipation of loss
- Typically starts 4–6 weeks before the partner leaves
- Time of increased tension
- Partner left behind may feel angry, depressed, resentful, irritable, etc
- Partner going away may feel guilty, anxious and panicked about to-do list
- Important to communicate during this stage and find out what the other is thinking and feeling
- Agree on how you will communicate while away from each other
- Organise special time together before moment of departure
- Decide together how you will guard yourselves against unfaithfulness while apart

1. *The Emotional Cycle of Deployment* is based on a study conducted by Kathleen Vestal Logan

EXERCISE 2

Protecting Your Marriage

Discuss how you will protect your marriage from temptation while you're apart. What are your concerns? What do you need to decide is off-limits for each of you?

Stage 2: Time immediately before departure

- Key features are emotional detachment and withdrawal
- Some create emotional distance as a way of preparing themselves for the moment of separation
- Partner going away may be experiencing a lot of guilt about leaving as well as concern about deployment
- Spend time seeking to understand rather than attacking each other
- Decide in advance how to say final goodbyes

EXERCISE 3

Separation Evaluation

Write down your first thought / answer to complete the statements below. Don't think too hard; you should give your immediate response, not the answer you think you should give. When you have both completed the evaluation separately, spend some time discussing your answers.

1. The thought of being apart for a significant period of time makes me feel...

_____

_____

_____

Please turn over →

EXERCISE 3 (continued)

2. The things that worry me most about being apart are...

3. I deal with separation by...

4. When we are apart, I receive most of my (emotional) support from...

5. The effects of separation on our marriage can be eased when you...

6. When we are apart the things I miss most are...

7. The effects of separation are not always negative. The positive
   aspects which separation brings to our marriage are...

Stage 3: Immediate effects of separation
- No matter how well prepared a couple is, they will probably feel shocked and unprepared for separation
- Likely to be a very busy period for partner who has gone away
- May be little time to dwell on their partner or even their own emotions
- Partner left at home may feel a sense of relief that departure has happened, together with feeling numb, aimless, irritable or overwhelmed
- Old routines have been disturbed and new ones not yet established
- May feel resentful of partner who has gone away
- Need to begin to make plans, particularly regarding how to spend weekends

Stage 4: Establishing a new routine
- The partner left behind 'gets on with it'
- Stress levels at home usually decrease and partner left at home becomes increasingly confident as they adjust
- Separation becomes bearable and emotions plateau
- Those with a partner in a combat zone should limit the amount of news listened to or watched on TV

Stage 5: Anticipation of homecoming
- Time of mixed emotions – apprehension and excitement
- The returning partner can experience anxiety, wondering if they are really needed at home
- Those left at home often realise they have not completed all their tasks before their partner's return
- Many wives anticipate reunion in terms of affection and reassurance – usually want to delay sex until emotionally reconnected
- Many husbands anticipate reconnecting through making love
- Be prepared to talk about your experiences when you were separated and how being apart has changed you
- Decide to show empathy and to practise good listening skills
- Generosity, understanding and sacrificial love needed on both sides

Time of Reunion

Tell each other what you look forward to most about your reunion and what you find most difficult.

Stage 6: Renegotiating roles and responsibilities

- Couple is now reunited
- Recognise the time it takes to readjust to having each other around again
- Important to show appreciation for way partner has handled time apart
- Share experiences and feelings to reconnect emotionally
- Move from being 'me' to 'us' again
- One or both partners may need some space to do their own thing
- Avoid thinking the other partner has easier role
- Re-negotiate roles and responsibilities

Notes

Identifying Roles

Read through the list below on your own.

- Write on the line the initial of the person you feel is responsible for this job when both partners are at home
- Where both share the task but one person does it more regularly, write both initials with the more active partner's initial listed first
- Where both are equally responsible write 'E'

Compare lists and discuss. Then look at the last column together and try to think of ways in which you can ease the pressure caused by some of these issues.

For example:

Earning money	R	Rhett currently is the only wage earner in our household
Grocery shopping	LR	Both do this, but Liesel does this most often
Refuelling car	E	Both take equal responsibility for this task

Task	Person normally responsible for task	Does responsibility for task change during separation?	How does this change make you feel? eg: ☺ or ☹	Practical measures you could take to ease the pressure of any stressful role changes *eg: set up all bills to be paid by direct debit during separation*
Earning money				
Grocery shopping				
Refuelling car				

Please turn over

Task	Person normally responsible for task	Does responsibility for task change during separation?	How does this change make you feel? eg: ☺ or ☹	**Practical measures you could take to ease the pressure of any stressful role changes** *eg: set up all bills to be paid by direct debit during separation*
Housework				
Disciplining children				
Booking holidays				
Contacting parents / in-laws				
Moving house				
Managing children's activities				
Tidying house				
Paying bills				
Laundry				
Ironing				
Putting children to bed				

EXERCISE 5 (continued)

Washing-up / doing dishwasher				
Choosing and buying furniture				
Cooking				
DIY				
Putting out rubbish				
Car maintenance / washing				
Mowing lawn / gardening				
Paying off credit card(s)				
Map-reading				
Driving				
Writing thank-you letters				
Other tasks:				

Stage 7: Establishing normal life together

- New routines are in place; roles have been re-negotiated
- Back on the same track emotionally
- Good things can come from time apart – marriages can grow through the experience

Notes

Marriage Time
Coping With Times of Separation – Homework

EXERCISE 1

Dealing with the Effects of Separation on Your Marriage

Each of you should fill in the first three questions on your own and then exchange your answers.

1. What keeps me going (or even excites me!) when I think of another period of time apart?

_____

_____

_____

Identify at least one opportunity that time apart offers that would be unlikely to happen without separation.

_____

_____

_____

Please turn over

2. What could be put into place to alleviate the worries and concerns identified in Exercise 3, Question 2: *'The things that worry me most about being apart are...'?*

   For example:
   'My worry about how to go about household or car repairs could be alleviated by making a list of useful contact numbers or simple instructions to follow prior to departure; My worry about missing a child's birth or other special occasions could be alleviated by saving money to buy a video camera to record the events.'

   _____

   _____

   _____

3. Identify three ways in which you would most like your partner to express their love in a romantic way while you are apart:

   For example:
   * Sending flowers or cards
   * Planning a special holiday to enjoy together when the time apart ends
   * Writing regular letters

   1. _____

   2. _____

   3. _____

4. Finally, if you haven't done so already, write or update your will. A will is the best way of protecting those you love in the unlikely event of your death. It does not necessarily cost anything to make a will, although there are certain criteria you must meet to ensure your document is legal. Further information can generally be found online.

If you are interested in finding out more about The Marriage Course or The Marriage Preparation Course (designed for engaged couples), where they are running or how to start up a course, please contact:

The Marriage Course Department
Alpha International
HTB Brompton Road
London SW7 1JA

Tel: **0845 644 7544**
Email: **info@themarriagecourse.org**
Website: **themarriagecourse.org**

If you are interested in finding out more about the Christian faith and would like to be put in touch with your nearest Alpha, please contact:

The Alpha Office
HTB Brompton Road
London SW7 1JA

Tel: **0845 644 7544**
Website: **alpha.org**